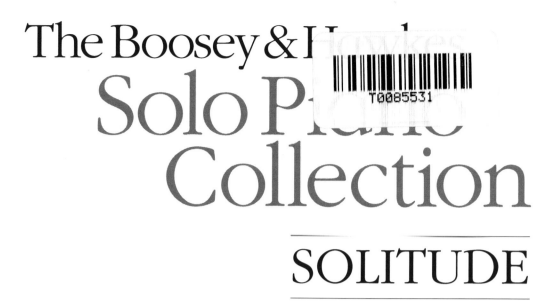

The Boosey & Hawkes
Solo Piano
Collection

SOLITUDE

and other well-known relaxing classics
arranged for the intermediate pianist

Boosey & Hawkes Music Publishers Ltd
www.boosey.com

ARRANGER BIOGRAPHIES

HYWEL DAVIES

Hywel Davies is an award-winning composer, arranger and creative artist. His compositions have been performed by a wealth of ensembles including Kororo (Bournemouth Symphony Orchestra's new music ensemble, with whom he has a long-standing association), and have been broadcast internationally by the BBC, CBC (Canada) and ABC (Australia). In 2003 he was the recipient of an Arts Council England International Fellowship. As an arranger, Davies has been published by Boosey & Hawkes, Durand-Salabert-Eschig, Chester Music, Novello, the Associated Board of the Royal Schools of Music and Music Sales. Recent projects for Boosey & Hawkes have included *Folk Roots for Flute* & *Folk Roots for Clarinet*, two volumes of pieces by Ástor Piazzolla (*El viaje* & *Vuelvo al sur*), and a volume of works by Rachmaninoff (*Play Rachmaninoff*); he has also compiled several anthologies of piano music including most recently *Ballet & Other Dances* and *Rachmaninoff* from the *Boosey & Hawkes Solo Piano Collection*. Davies is in demand as a sonic and installation artist, and has received commissions from organisations including Arts Council England and the National Trust.

www.hyweldavies.co.uk

CAROL KLOSE

Carol Klose is an accomplished performer, teacher, composer and arranger. Formerly a member of staff at Wisconsin College Conservatory of Music, Carol has spent over 30 years working in the field of music publishing and has a large number of compositions and arrangements in print, many of which are published by Hal Leonard.

CHRISTOPHER NORTON

Christopher Norton was born in New Zealand in 1953. After graduating he began his career as a teacher, pianist and composer, and began to develop an interest in popular music. Coming to the UK in 1977 on a university scholarship, he studied composition at York University with Wilfred Mellers and David Blake. Well established as a composer, producer, arranger and educationalist, Norton has written stage musicals, ballet scores, piano music, popular songs and orchestral music as well as jingles and signature tunes for TV and radio. He has lectured all over the world on aspects of his work and likes to integrate traditional teaching methods with aspects of modern technology. Chris is best known for his world-famous series *Microjazz* — easy graded pieces in modern styles such as blues, rock 'n' roll, reggae and jazz — and for his award-winning *Essential Guides to Pop Styles*, *Latin Styles* and *Jazz Styles*.

www.christophernorton.com

Published by Boosey & Hawkes Music Publishers Ltd
Aldwych House
71–91 Aldwych
London
WC2B 4HN

www.boosey.com

© Copyright 2013 by Boosey & Hawkes Music Publishers Ltd

ISMN 979-0-060-12389-4
ISBN 978-0-85162-654-3

This impression 2020

Printed by Halstan:
Halstan UK, 2–10 Plantation Road, Amersham, Bucks, HP6 6HJ. United Kingdom
Halstan DE, Weißliliengasse 4, 55116 Mainz. Germany

Music origination by Jon Bunker
Cover design by Fresh Lemon

CONTENTS

ADAGIO

TOMASO ALBINONI
(1671–1751)
arranged by Hywel Davies

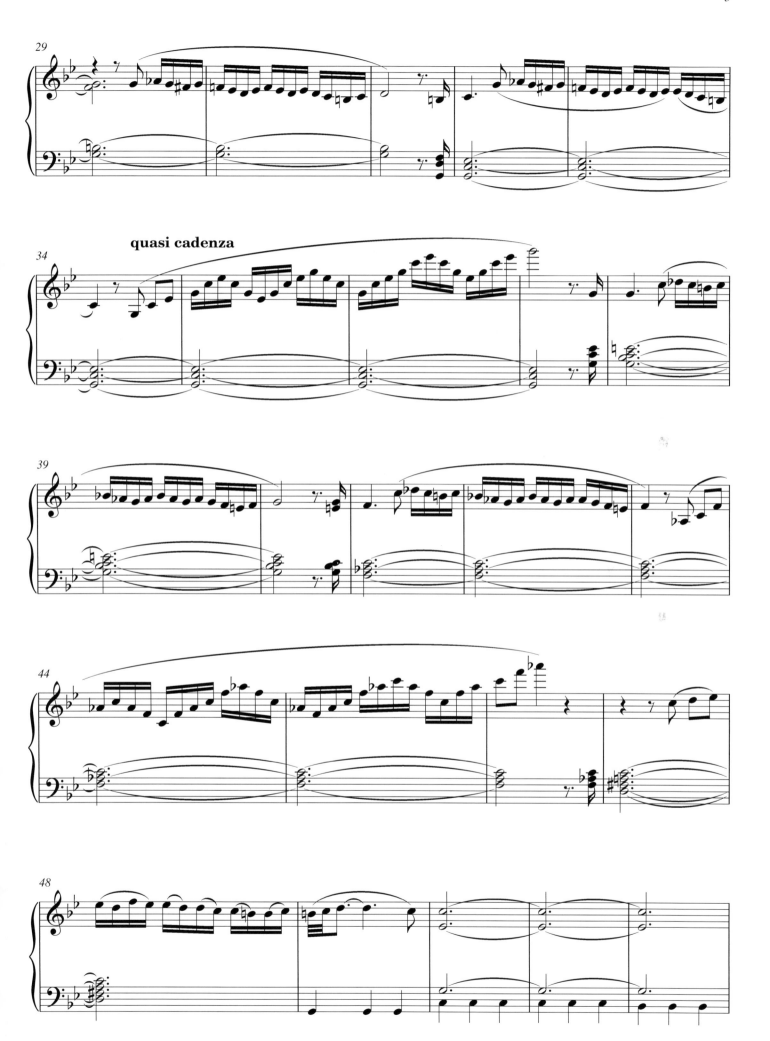

quasi cadenza

AIR ON A G STRING

JOHANN SEBASTIAN BACH
(1685–1750)
arranged by Hywel Davies

GOLDBERG VARIATIONS
Aria

JOHANN SEBASTIAN BACH
(1685–1750)
arranged by Hywel Davies

[poco rit]

WEST SIDE STORY
Somewhere

LEONARD BERNSTEIN
(1918–1990)
arranged by Carol Klose

Slowly, with reverence

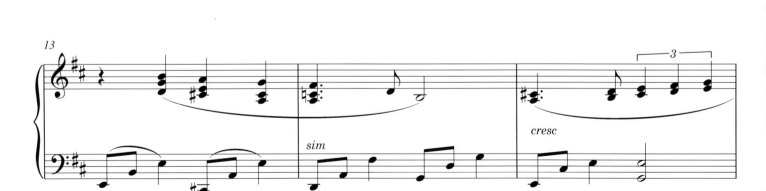

Poco più mosso

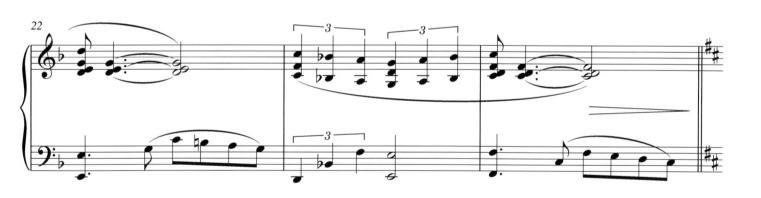

rit

Tempo I

SIMPLE GIFTS
Like a prayer

AARON COPLAND
(1900–1990)

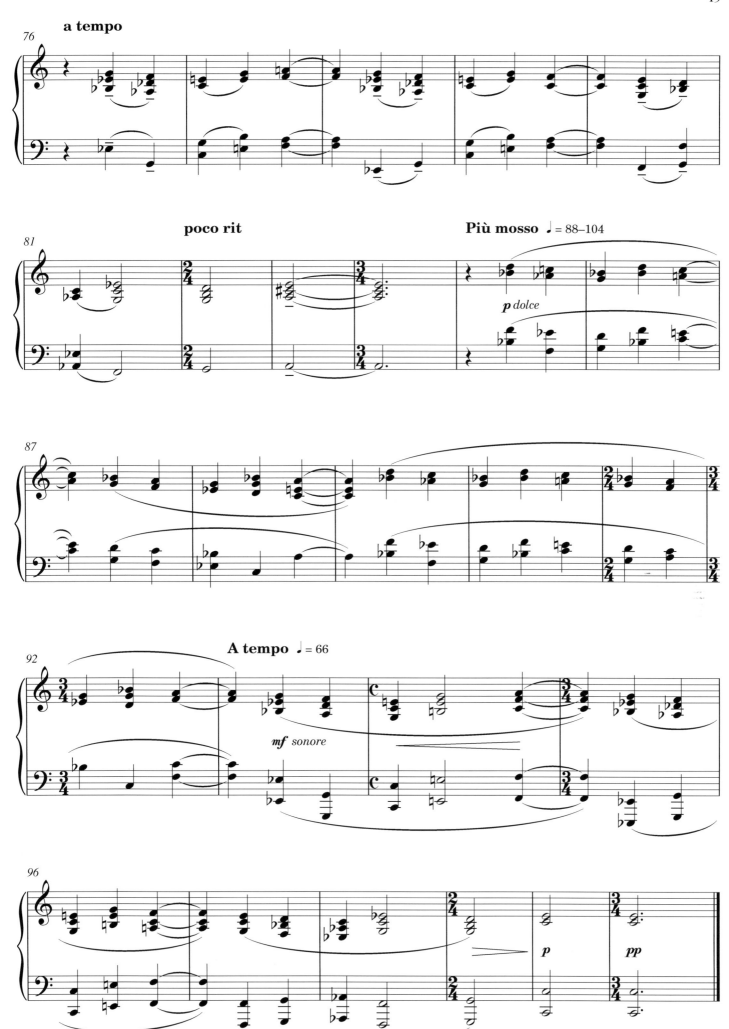

A HYMN TO THE VIRGIN

BENJAMIN BRITTEN
(1913–1976)
arranged by Hywel Davies

CLAIR DE LUNE

CLAUDE DEBUSSY
(1862–1918)
arranged by Hywel Davies

Andante très expressif

una corda

Tempo rubato

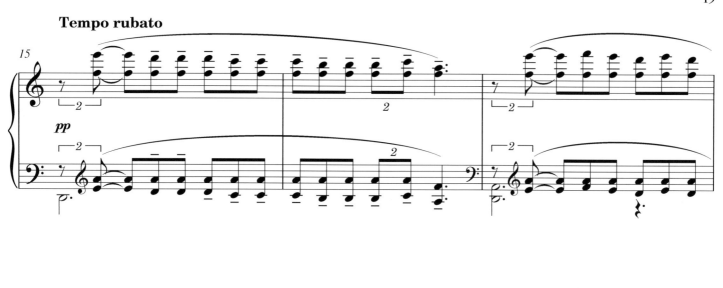

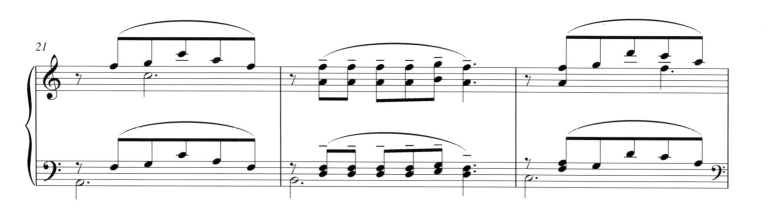

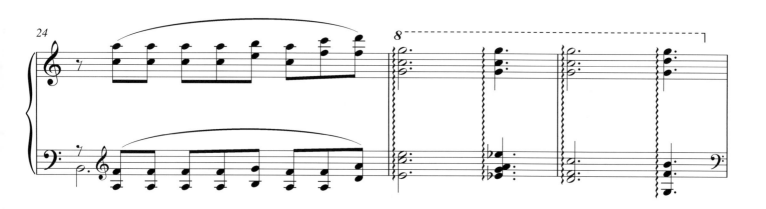

Un poco mosso

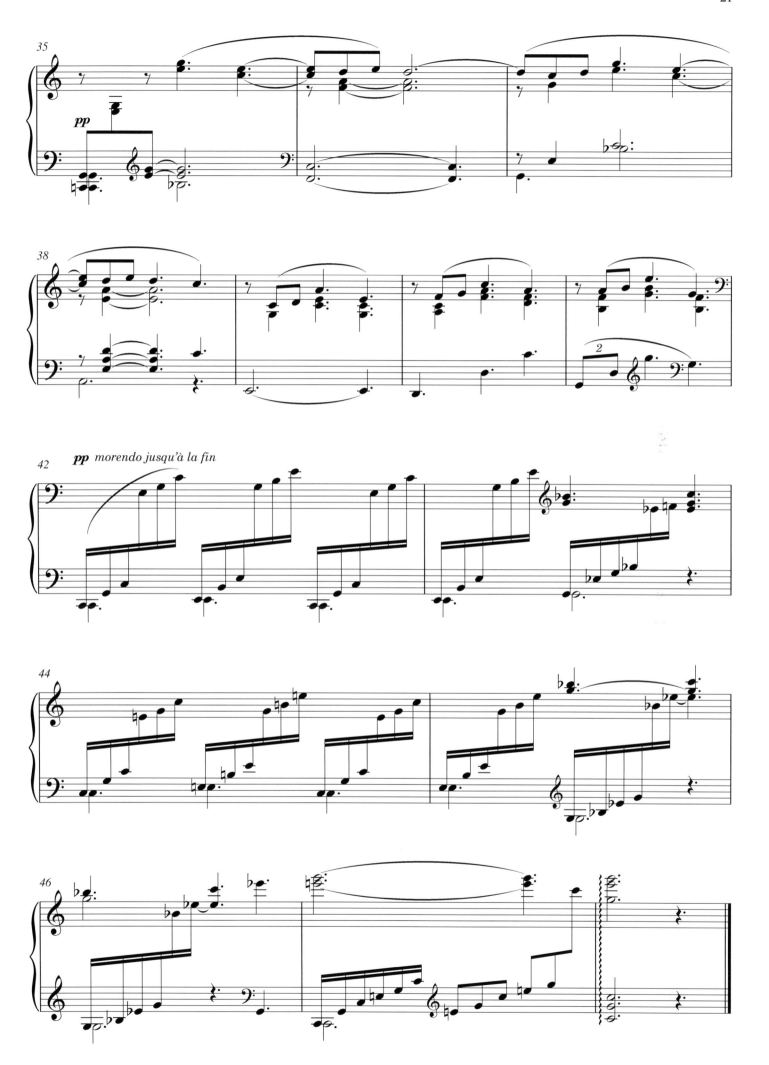

COPPELIA
Waltz

LÉO DELIBES
(1836–1891)
arranged by Hywel Davies

CHANSON DE MATIN

EDWARD ELGAR
(1857–1934)
arranged by Hywel Davies

SOLITUDE

DUKE ELLINGTON
(1899–1974)
arranged by Hywel Davies

In time but not fast

con Ped

rit

Much slower

PAVANE

GABRIEL FAURÉ
(1845–1924)
arranged by Hywel Davies

ECLOGUE

GERALD FINZI
(1901–1956)
arranged by Hywel Davies

Andante semplice ♩ = 46

ritard molto   **a tempo, ma poch più movimento**

ritard molto   Tempo I

ritard molto

PIANO CONCERTO IN F
Theme from second movement

GEORGE GERSHWIN
(1898–1937)
arranged by Hywel Davies

MOONGLOW

WILL HUDSON (1908-1981)
IRVING MILLS (1894-1985)
& EDDIE DE LANGE (1904-1949)
arranged by Hywel Davies

Slow and free

Gentle swing

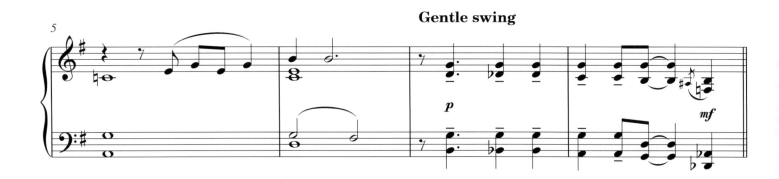

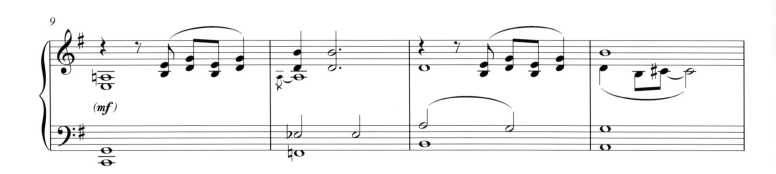

RHAPSODY IN BLUE
Theme

GEORGE GERSHWIN
(1898–1937)
arranged by Hywel Davies

Moderately, slow, with expression

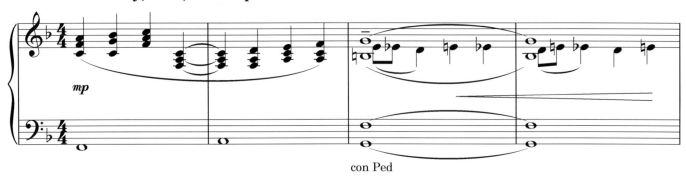

con Ped

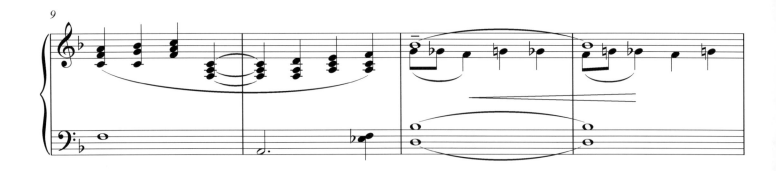

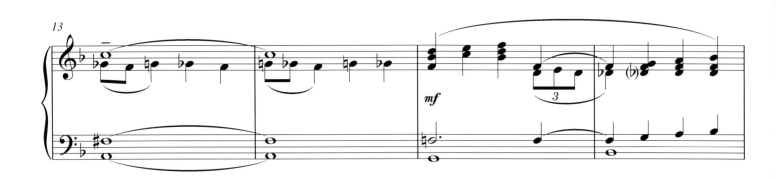

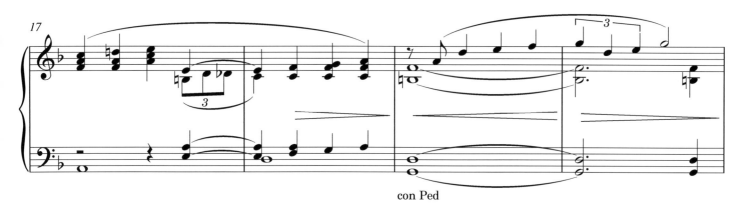

con Ped

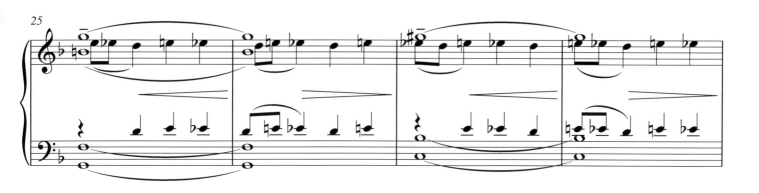

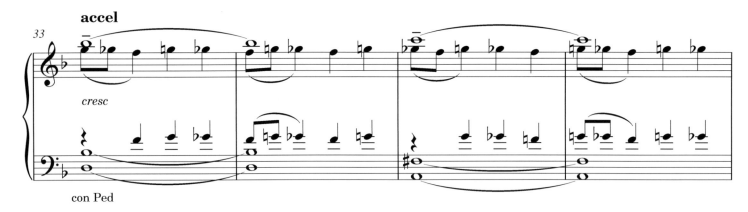

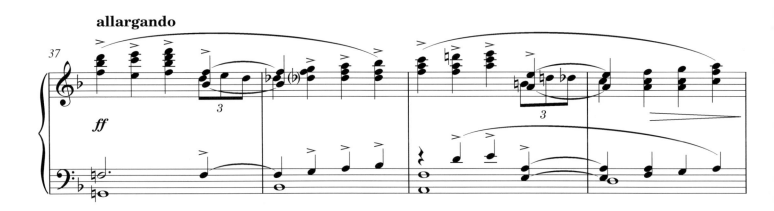

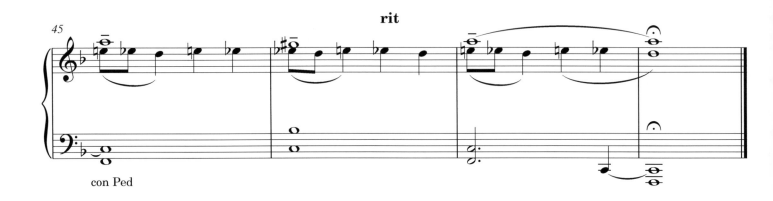

THE PEACEMAKERS
Solitude

KARL JENKINS
(b 1944)
arranged by Hywel Davies

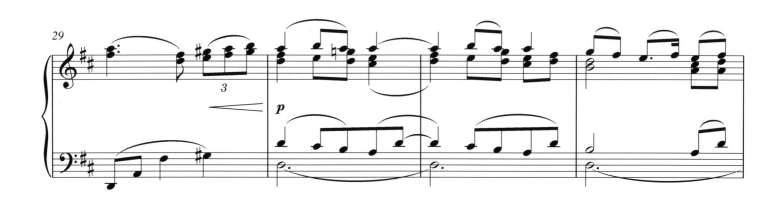

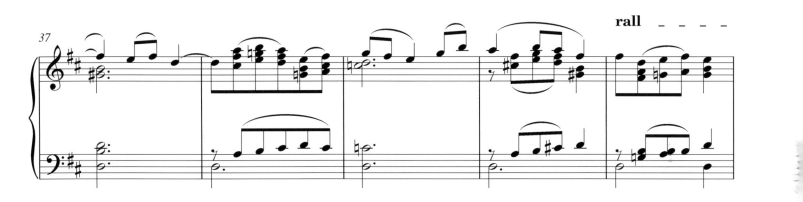

SONGS OF SANCTUARY
Adiemus

KARL JENKINS
(b 1944)
arranged by Hywel Davies

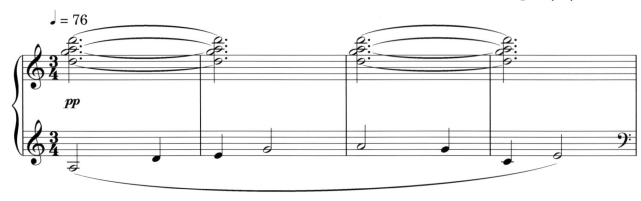

WILD SWANS SUITE
Eliza Aria

ELENA KATS-CHERNIN
(b 1957)

SPARTICUS & PHRYGIA
Adagio

ARAM KHACHATURIAN
(1903–1978)
arranged by Hywel Davies

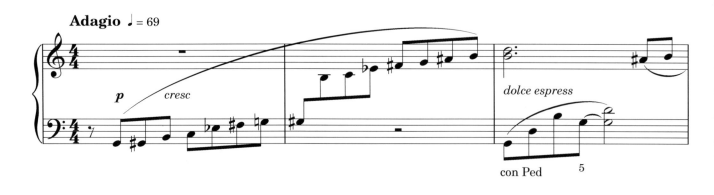

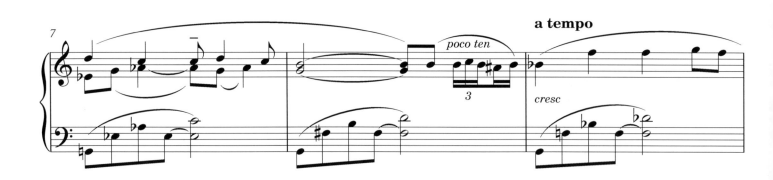

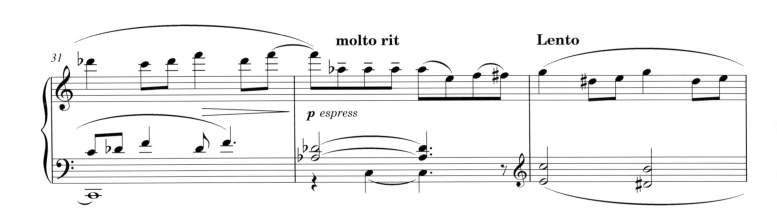

CALM WATER
Stevie's Ferry to Hoy

PETER MAXWELL DAVIES
(b 1934)

CONCERTO FOR ORCHESTRA
Largo

ZOLTÁN KODÁLY
(1882–1967)
arranged by Hywel Davies

BARNELCUPÉDIE

JAMES MACMILLAN
(b 1959)

FAREWELL TO STROMNESS

PETER MAXWELL DAVIES
(b 1934)

CANON IN D

JOHANN PACHELBEL
(1653-1706)
arranged by Hywel Davies

[Largo ♩ = 44]

ROMEO AND JULIET
Madrigal

SERGE PROKOFIEFF
(1891–1953)
arranged by Hywel Davies

ROMEO AND JULIET
Balcony Scene

SERGE PROKOFIEFF
(1891–1953)
arranged by Hywel Davies

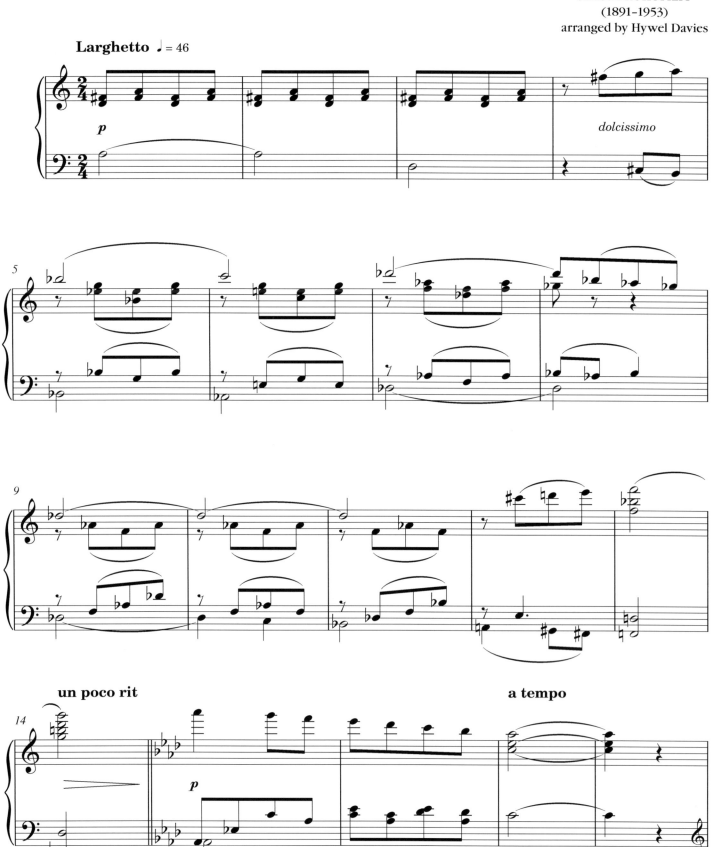

PIANO CONCERTO No 2
Theme from third movement

SERGEI RACHMANINOFF
(1873–1943)
arranged by Christopher Norton

RHAPSODY ON A THEME OF PAGANINI
Variation 18

SERGEI RACHMANINOFF
(1873–1943)
arranged by Hywel Davies

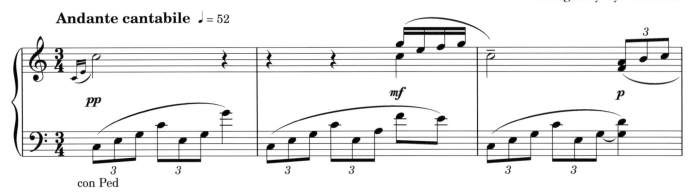

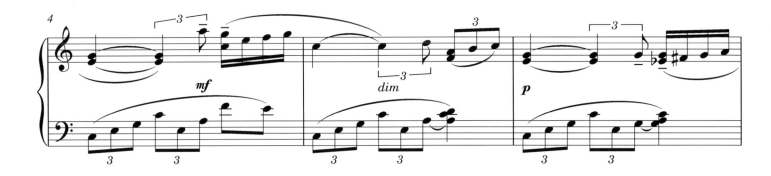

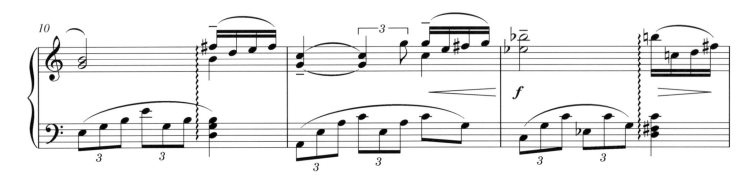

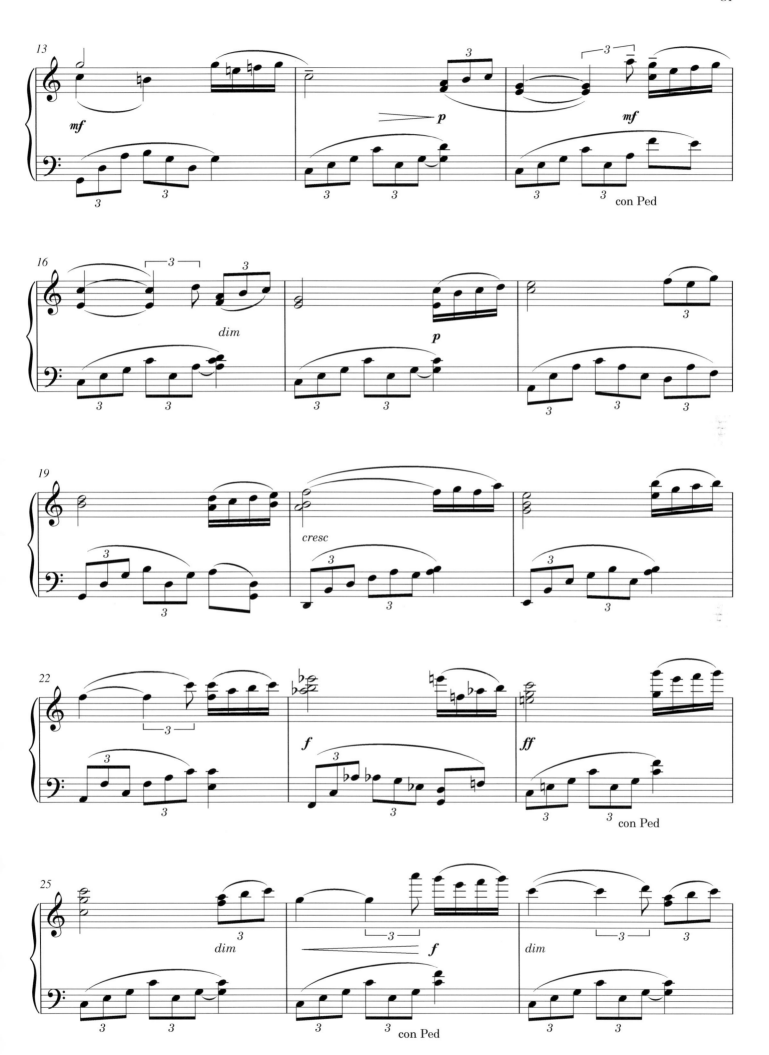

PIANO CONCERTO No 2
Theme from second movement

DMITRI SHOSTAKOVICH
(1906–1975)
arranged by Christopher Norton

Andante ♩ = 76

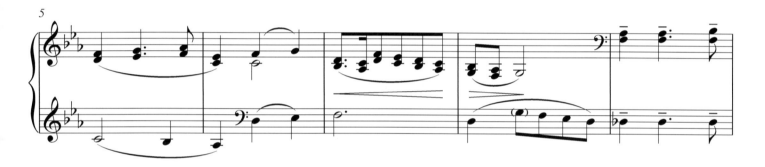

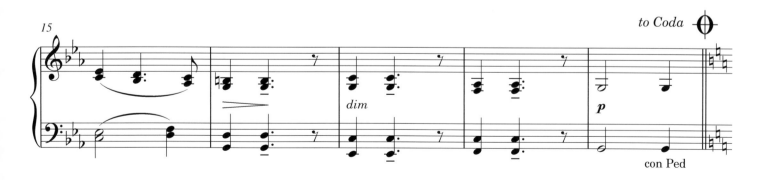

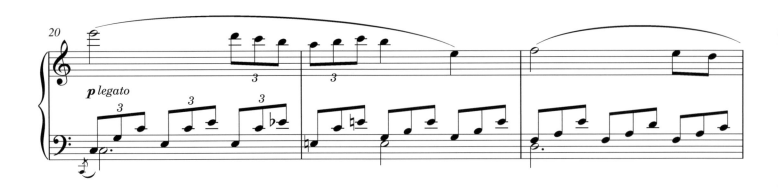

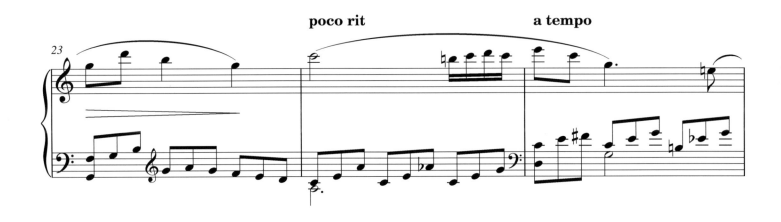

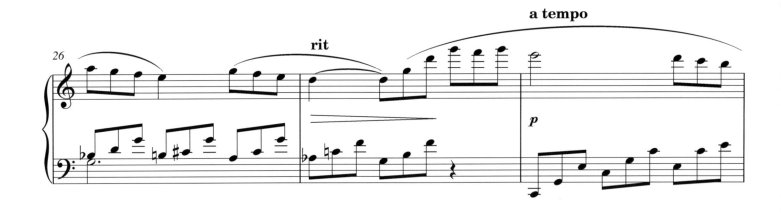

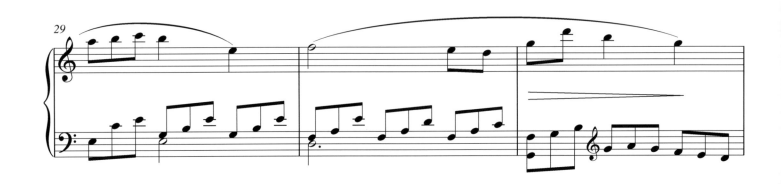

DC al Coda

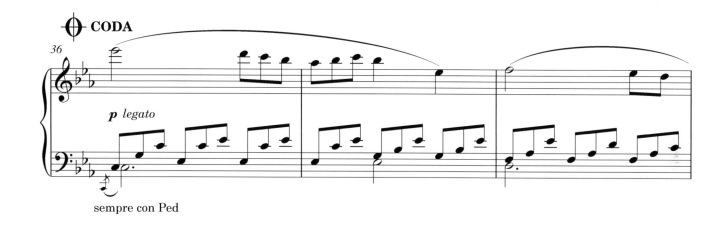

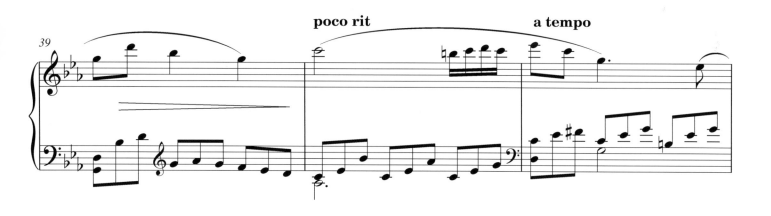

GYMNOPÉDIE No 1

ERIK SATIE
(1866–1925)
arranged by Hywel Davies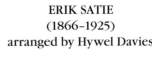

Lent et doulourex

GADFLY
Romance

DMITRI SHOSTAKOVICH
(1906–1975)
arranged by Hywel Davies

FALL OF BERLIN
In the garden

DMITRI SHOSTAKOVICH
(1906–1975)
arranged by Hywel Davies

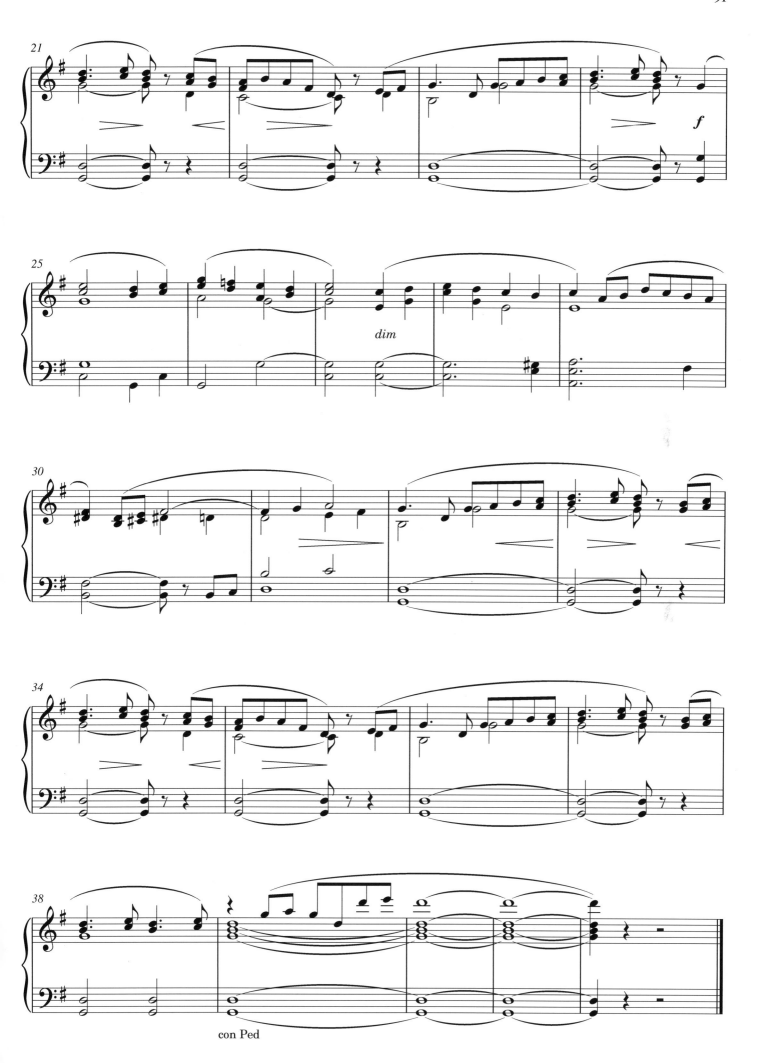

con Ped

LE BAISER DE LA FÉE
The fairy's kiss

IGOR STRAVINSKY
(1882–1971)
arranged by Christopher Norton

Twentieth-Century Works for Piano

Bartók

For Children (volumes 1 & 2)
A new edition of Bartók's classic piano pieces. Revised with new engraving and editorial notes by the composer's son, Peter Bartók

Mikrokosmos (volumes 1–6)
The definitive edition of the piano teaching classic. Includes an introduction by Peter Bartók

Kabalevsky

Easy Piano Compositions
Contains *Four Little Pieces* op 14, *Twenty-four Little Pieces* op 39 and *Four Rondos* op 60

Maxwell Davies

Stevie's Ferry to Hoy
Three simple pieces – *Calm Water*, *Choppy Seas* and *Safe Landing* – with all the drama of a short journey by sea

Prokofieff

Musiques d'enfants
A piano repertoire classic published in the Russian Piano Classics series. With introductions and performance notes by Peter Donohoe

Peter and the Wolf (arranged by Carol Barratt)
Prokofieff's classic children's tale in a charming new picture book edition. The piano music is faithfully arranged by Carol Barratt and the story is retold through verse with stunning full colour illustrations throughout

Rachmaninoff

Play Rachmaninoff
Nine of Rachmaninoff's greatest themes arranged for the intermediate standard pianist. Includes Piano Concerto no 3 (theme from *Shine*), Symphony no 2 (theme from movement 3), *Vocalise* and more

various

20th-Century Easy Piano Collection
A superb collection of music from some of the most important composers of the last century. Includes pieces by 20th-century masters as well as less familiar names and young composers of the current generation

20th-Century Classics (volumes 1 & 2)
Well known themes from 20th-century classics arranged for solo piano. Includes Britten's *A Young Person's Guide to the Orchestra* and Copland's *Hoe Down*. Also available arranged for piano duet

Boosey & Hawkes Music Publishers Ltd
www.boosey.com